SECRET*

*All the pure uranium metal to be had in 1941 came from the
laboratory of a Westinghouse lamp plant at Bloomfield, N. J.*

SECRET *

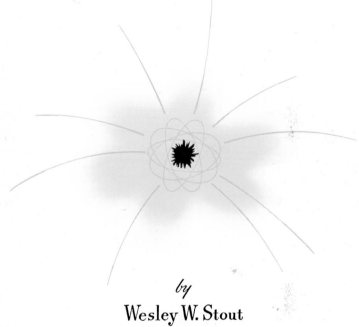

by
Wesley W. Stout

Chrysler Corporation

Detroit, Michigan

1947

Foreword

IN the tremendous endeavor which produced the atom bomb, and thus brought World War II to a sudden close, Chrysler Corporation had an important part.

This is a simple narrative of what was done to give man his first control over the energy locked in the atom.

The presence of this new force at man's command, and the stark terror that imagination gives to atomic weapons carried to their still distant ultimate development, has stirred anew the determination of good men to create at long last in the world a state of permanent peace.

Peace never has been made by outlawing a given weapon. History shows new wars beginning where old ones left off. To keep peace men must honestly recognize and eliminate the things they do and that nations do which culminate in bloodshed. Perhaps the dire possibilities of atom power will some day bring men to this point.

Meantime science and industry will be working on ways to employ the atom's energy for men's benefit; ways that might even in time utterly overshadow the first destructive application.

K. T. KELLER
President

Test Baker—Bikini—July 1946

Part of the huge Hanford, Washington, plutonium works, built in a sage brush desert and (below) the U-shaped gaseous diffusion U-253 plant at Oak Ridge, Tenn., for which Chrysler built the diffusers.

* The text of this book has been reviewed and permission for its publication has been given by the U. S. Army, Corps of Engineers, for the War Department.

The war ended, in effect, in the New Mexican desert at dawn of July 16, 1945, when the first atomic bomb was set off experimentally. What followed at Hiroshima on August 6th, and at Nagasaki three days later, was, like the formal Japanese surrender in another five days, predestined four weeks earlier at Alamogordo.

Chrysler Corporation was a major industrial contributor to the atomic bomb itself, as well as the largest source of the engines which powered the B-29 Superfortresses which dropped the bombs.

The bomb first was proposed to Chrysler in the spring of 1943. The top war secret of all, it was known within the Corporation only as X-100 and all knowledge of its nature and purpose limited to a few key men.

What may come of atomic fission, for good or for evil, is enough to stagger any imagination, but the atomic bomb itself is no awesome mystery. Its how and why can be understood by any one who doesn't shut his ears and mind.

If you think of the tapping of atomic energy as a detective story, the first meager clues were found

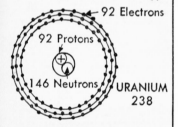

RADIOACTIVITY
RADIUM NUCLEUS

Alpha particles
Beta particles
Gamma rays
Lighter nucleus

Some unstable "heavy" atoms voluntarily split to form other atoms and release usable energy

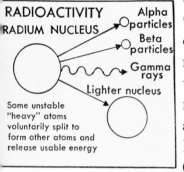

NATURE'S HEAVIEST ATOM
Basic Source of Atomic Energy

92 Electrons
92 Protons
146 Neutrons
URANIUM 238

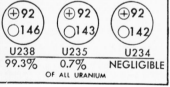

ISOTOPES

Chemically the same element and their nuclei contain the same number of protons. Only the number of neutrons differs. Thus the uranium isotopes are:

⊕92 ◯146	⊕92 ◯143	⊕92 ◯142
U238	U235	U234
99.3%	0.7%	NEGLIGIBLE

OF ALL URANIUM

MCGRAW-HILL PHOTO

about fifty years ago when a German, William Roentgen, discovered the X-ray and a Frenchman, Antoine Becquerel, discovered what we call radioactivity when he found uranium salts had developed a photographic plate in the dark. From this point, Pierre and Marie Curie, pupils of Becquerel, went on to discover radium, the first known radioactive element and always present in uranium.

How to account for radioactivity, this giving off of faint charged particles? Science deduced that this energy could be nothing less than a breaking down of the element, a conception which stood the science of physics on its head; for all the elements in Nature, her basic building blocks, had been thought to be unchanging and unchangeable.

As radium dissipates its energy, it eventually turns into lead, but this natural decay is very, very slow. Dangerous to human flesh and bone as exposure to radium is, a gram of it would be one hundred years in giving off enough heat to boil a small cup of water. So no one then dreamed of trying to harness mechanically such a feeble force.

What is an atom? Everything is made up of invisibly small particles. We call these particles atoms from the Greek root meaning "uncuttable," and when many of us were in school we still were taught that the atom is the least particle existing in Nature; that it was indivisible. Yet as early as 1900, Sir J. J. Thompson, the British physicist, had identified the electron, a minute particle of the atom. By 1918 his pupil, Lord Rutherford, had chipped a fragment from an atom and discovered the proton, another particle. And in 1932 Sir James Chadwick discovered a third particle which he called a neutron.

Rutherford had reasoned on circumstantial evidence that the atom must consist of a number of negatively charged electrons flying around a central charged body, the nucleus or core. Now we know that this is true, and we know much more. This tiny core is only one five-thousandth part of the atom in size, though it is so dense that it contains nearly all the atom's weight. The rest is empty space enclosed by a cloud of electrons which move around the nucleus much as the earth and the other planets move around our sun.

The positively charged nucleus and the negative electrons attract each other, but the electrons are held out in their orbits by the centrifugal force of their great speed, something as the earth is held away from the strong pull of the sun.

The nucleus itself is made up of two kinds of smaller particles, as many as 200 of them, tightly locked together. Some are Rutherford's positively charged protons, others are Chadwick's neutrons, which are neither positive nor negative. Imprisoned in each of these cells is a force many thousand times more powerful than the pull of gravity, a force that seems to be the ultimate source of all life and energy.

Though all atoms are made up of the same three parts—protons, neutrons and electrons—each of the 96 known elements (four new ones have been found or created since 1938) has its own atom. It is the proportion of protons which makes one element differ from another. That is to say, except that both are heavy, gold and mercury are as unalike as night and day, yet the difference between them is one proton only. If you could knock off one of the 80 protons which play on the mercury team you would have an atom of gold. Or if you could chip off one proton from the eight in an atom of oxygen you would have an atom of nitrogen.

For each proton in the core there is one electron in the cloud flying around the core, for plus and minus must balance in the atom. In other words, hydrogen, lightest of known elements, has one proton in its nucleus and only one electron planet while uranium, heaviest element known until recently, has 92 protons and 92 planet electrons flying around its core.

No one has ever seen an atom, let alone a proton, a neutron or an electron. This is far beyond the power

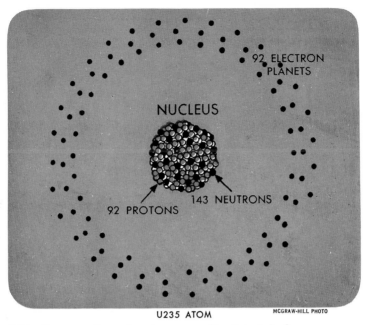

92 ELECTRON PLANETS

NUCLEUS

92 PROTONS

143 NEUTRONS

U235 ATOM   MCGRAW-HILL PHOTO

This diagram of an atom is necessarily distorted; the core or nucleus actually is only one five-thousandth part of the atom in size.

of the strongest existing microscope. And if Science often has been wrong in the past, why should we believe what it now says about something no one can see, feel, taste or smell?

Well, no Jap is in a doubting mood. The atomic bomb should be its own proof to a layman, for it began with deductions no one could prove by any of the senses. Acting on these theoretical assumptions, Science put the bomb together, prevented it from exploding in the process, exploded it at the desired moment, got exactly the result it had foreseen.

Science doesn't pretend to know all about the atom as yet. In fact, only lately it has identified still further

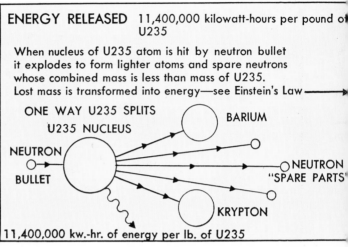

ENERGY RELEASED 11,400,000 kilowatt-hours per pound of U235

When nucleus of U235 atom is hit by neutron bullet it explodes to form lighter atoms and spare neutrons whose combined mass is less than mass of U235. Lost mass is transformed into energy—see Einstein's Law ⟶

ONE WAY U235 SPLITS

U235 NUCLEUS

NEUTRON BULLET

BARIUM

NEUTRON "SPARE PARTS"

KRYPTON

11,400,000 kw.-hr. of energy per lb. of U235

and smaller atomic sub-particles it is calling positrons, mesotrons and neutrinos. But there could have been no bomb if these major assumptions had not been true.

The first of these was reasoned out in 1905 by Albert Einstein, whose name is likely to be as famous to our descendants as that of Galileo and Newton. In the same year that Rutherford first foresaw the structure of the atom, Einstein announced his conclusion that mass and energy are different forms of the same thing.

It has been said that no more than ten minds in the world can grasp some of the Einstein theorems, but this is not one such. He was saying that all matter in the universe is locked-up energy and that all energy (which includes light and heat) is unlocked or dissipated matter. As all matter is made up of atoms, this energy is frozen in the atom. How he thought this through is beyond understanding by all but a few, but the conclusion is reasonably simple.

Einstein knew no way of unlocking this energy, but by his prophetic calculation of more than forty years ago, if 2.2 pounds (1 kilogram) of any matter could be converted into energy by the breaking down of its atoms, it would produce unbelievable power, as much as all the electrical generating capacity of the United States for two months. A lifetime's fuel for an automobile could be carried in a fountain pen. A cup of water could drive a liner across the Atlantic and back.

This seemed to have about as much practical value as the medieval speculation as to how many angels could stand on the head of a pin until, in 1919, Lord Rutherford announced that it should be possible artificially to cause small leaks of energy from stable elements by bombarding them with the particles

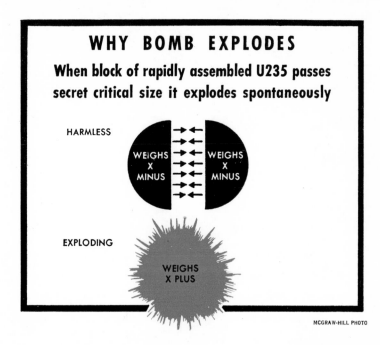

WHY BOMB EXPLODES

When block of rapidly assembled U235 passes
secret critical size it explodes spontaneously

HARMLESS

WEIGHS X MINUS   WEIGHS X MINUS

EXPLODING

WEIGHS X PLUS

MCGRAW-HILL PHOTO

thrown off by radium in its course of slow natural decomposition into lead.

Which means that Rutherford was predicting that man could tap the energy locked-up in the atom, though only in infinitesimally small amounts.

By 1934, the Curies' daughter, Irene, and her husband, Frederique Joliot, had followed the Rutherford trail to the point where they had made stable elements radioactive, giving off particles and radiation like radium.

Now the story moves down to the University of Rome where Dr. Enrico Fermi shortly got a more exciting result by bombarding a speck of uranium with Chadwick's newly identified neutrons, and by first slowing these neutrons down.

To understand what he did, let's go back to 1919 and Rutherford, first man to chip a fragment off an atom. His great difficulty and the great difficulty of all physicists down to Fermi, was to score a direct hit. He found that he had to shoot a million sub-atomic particles from radium to get one bull's-eye. As late as 1934, Dr. Einstein complained that it was like "trying to shoot birds in the dark in a country where there were not many birds in the sky." The odds seemed so long that Einstein then wondered if man ever should succeed in releasing atomic energy in useful amounts.

Rutherford got his first hint of the atom's structure when he fired radium rays through a thin sheet of mica. They should have passed through this flimsy barrier like a battleship's shell through a canvas sail, yet he found their direction was changed slightly. They must be striking something strong enough to deflect them. Later, one of his assistants repeated the experiment with a thin sheet of gold—which should have been just as easy as mica for an atomic particle —and the rays were bent even more.

Recognizing this as an important clue to some mystery, Rutherford asked his assistant to repeat the experiment with great care, and this time some of the radium particles bounced back without penetrating the gold film. They had been thrown for a loss.

"It was quite the most incredible event that had ever happened to me," he said many years later. "On consideration, I realized that it must be the result of a single concussion, and when I had made the calculations I saw that this was impossible unless you assumed that the greater part of the mass of the atom was concentrated in a minute nucleus."

When the Rutherford conjecture was followed through, Science found that the cloud of electrons moving about an atom's core protects the core from atomic projectiles much as sand bags shelter a soldier from bullets. This may be Nature's way of insuring that the universe is not blown up by cosmic rays, those atomic particles from other worlds which come hurtling through space with such terrific speed that they usually drive through our atmosphere and deep into the earth.

From 1919 down to Fermi's discovery, Science was building bigger and bigger atom-smashing machines to bombard atoms with streams of protons or other positively-charged particles with ever greater speed. This was thought to be necessary because the positively-charged particle had to batter its way into the atom's core.

But by using the neutral particle, the neutron, as a bullet and by first slowing it down by passing it through hydrogen, Fermi scored a direct hit every time on the core of the atom.

Fermi was not looking for the atomic bomb, nor were any of the other many experimenters. He was hoping to create from uranium one or two elements heavier than uranium and unknown in Nature, and he

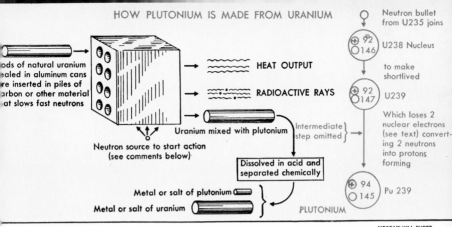

HOW PLUTONIUM IS MADE FROM URANIUM

Rods of natural uranium sealed in aluminum cans are inserted in piles of carbon or other material that slows fast neutrons

Neutron source to start action (see comments below)

Uranium mixed with plutonium

HEAT OUTPUT

RADIOACTIVE RAYS

Intermediate step omitted

Dissolved in acid and separated chemically

Metal or salt of plutonium

Metal or salt of uranium

PLUTONIUM

Neutron bullet from U235 joins

+92 O146 U238 Nucleus

to make shortlived

+92 O147 U239

Which loses 2 nuclear electrons (see text) converting 2 neutrons into protons forming

+94 O145 Pu 239

did get one such, an atom of 93 protons in its nucleus, one more than the protons in an uranium nucleus.

All over the world scientists now went to work with slowed-down neutrons. In Berlin, Prof. Otto Hahn, head of the great Kaiser Wilhelm Institute, assigned Dr. Lise Meitner to this research. The Nazis were in power and Dr. Meitner had Jewish blood, but Hahn managed to protect her until the end of 1938, when she was forced to flee to Stockholm, her work un-

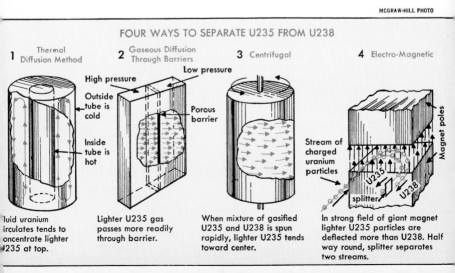

FOUR WAYS TO SEPARATE U235 FROM U238

1 Thermal Diffusion Method

2 Gaseous Diffusion Through Barriers

3 Centrifugal

4 Electro-Magnetic

High pressure

Low pressure

Outside tube is cold

Porous barrier

Inside tube is hot

Stream of charged uranium particles

Magnet poles

U235

U238

splitter

Fluid uranium circulates tends to concentrate lighter U235 at top.

Lighter U235 gas passes more readily through barrier.

When mixture of gasified U235 and U238 is spun rapidly, lighter U235 tends toward center.

In strong field of giant magnet lighter U235 particles are deflected more than U238. Half way round, splitter separates two streams.

The British and Norwegians spent many lives in raids on this Nazi atomic bomb plant at Rjukan, Norway.

finished. Hahn and Dr. F. Strassman took over her data and continued her research.

Hahn quickly identified barium in the result which followed the bombardment of a speck of uranium with slowed-down neutrons. This was the all-important basic clue to the atomic bomb, but as barium is not even distantly related to uranium, Hahn was not too sure but what barium had been present all along in the uranium as an impurity. He published his findings in a German journal in January of 1939, seeing to it that a copy went to Dr. Meitner in Sweden.

Until now the most powerful atom-smashing machine had done no more than knock a few particles off an atom, with a slow, tiny leak of energy, far less energy than that which went into the machine. But satisfied that no barium had been present in the uranium, Dr. Meitner reasoned that an atom of uranium actually must have been split roughly in half. And if one of the halves was barium, the other should be krypton because uranium has 92 protons, barium has 56 and krypton has 36; subtract 56 from 92 and you have 36.

This was sensational enough, but if an atom had been split in this manner, then, by the Einstein theorem, a great burst of energy should have been released—by rough estimate, about 200 million electron volts. The electron volt is a new yardstick, meaning the amount of force needed to move one

Brig. Gen. T. F. Farrell, who commanded the atombombing of Japan; Mr. Keller; Col., now General, K. D. Nichols of the Manhattan Project; and Comm. F. L. Ashworth, ranking officer on the Nagasaki bombing flight.

electron through a potential difference of one volt. And that brings up the fact that we now know what electricity is. Until the day before yesterday we knew only what it did, but nuclear physics has shown that it is a stream of electrons in motion. When you switch on a lamp, billions of electrons per second start bumping their way between the atoms of the copper wire to the lamp filaments.

By mail, Dr. Meitner discussed these conclusions with a confrere in Copenhagen, Dr. O. R. Frisch, also a refugee from Germany. Frisch is the son-in-law of Dr. Niels Bohr, one of the great names in atomic physics. Bohr had fled from Denmark by then and was in the United States working under the name of "Mr. Nicholas Baker" with Einstein at Princeton and with Fermi at Columbia. Fermi, who since has become an American citizen, was in exile from Fascist Italy.

Frisch was so excited that he cabled the substance of the Hahn-Meitner findings to his father-in-law. When the cable reached Dr. Bohr January 24, 1939, he quickly got in touch with Dr. George B. Pegram, dean of physics at Columbia, and Dr. John R. Dunning. Without knowing the full details of Dr. Meitner's calculations, they scribbled some figures on a pad and arrived independently at the same result. If the uranium atom had been split into barium and krypton, the parts should have flown apart like celestial cannon balls, each fragment travelling with a force close to 100 million electron volts. They proved it the next day in the laboratory.

Official artist's sketch of where, beneath the stands of Stagg Field stadium, University of Chicago, atomic fission first was accomplished in a chain reaction Dec. 6, 1942. Courtesy University of Chicago.

Two days later Dr. Bohr stampeded a conference on theoretical physics at George Washington University when he reported all. When his hearers began to appreciate what he was saying, most of them dashed from the auditorium to telephone their laboratories. In another 24 hours, a score of laboratories had confirmed that the atom had been split, with a high release of energy.

Yet something important was missing. If theory was right, when the atom was split, many high-speed atomic bullets in the form of neutrons should have been released and some of these should have split other atoms, starting a chain reaction like a string of firecrackers until all were blasted in a shocking explosion. This had not happened; only a release of energy greater than any before measured in a cyclotron.

Meanwhile, in 1935, Prof. Arthur J. Dempster of the University of Chicago had discovered by means of an "atomic microscope" that uranium contains three different kinds of atoms. Chemically, they are identical; they differ only in their number of neutrons. He called them U-238, U-235 and U-234, the sums of the combined number of protons and neutrons in their respective cores. More than 99% of uranium is U-238. There is only 1 part in 140 of U-235 and the barest trace of U-234.

Science called these off-beat atoms "isotopes" from the Greek for "same place." There are many of them in Nature. When radium, for example, turns into lead that lead can not be distinguished by any chemical test from ordinary lead, yet it has a slightly different atomic weight.

Dr. Bohr and Dr. J. A. Wheeler of Princeton reasoned that the less than 1% of U-235 in uranium must be the firebug which set off the blaze, the 99% plus of U-238 the fire department which put it out. This was pure deduction. It could be proved or disproved only by isolating U-235 in a pure state. This never had been done and it was questionable if it could be done, 238 and 235 being chemically the same.

But an international race to find a way began. It was won by a 27-year-old physicist at the University of Minnesota, Dr. Alfred O. Nier, with a sample much too minute to be seen by the eye. The General Electric laboratories shortly produced a slightly

Removing dangerous radio-active material produced in the University of Chicago pile; instrument in foreground is a Geiger counter. COURTESY UNIVERSITY OF CHICAGO

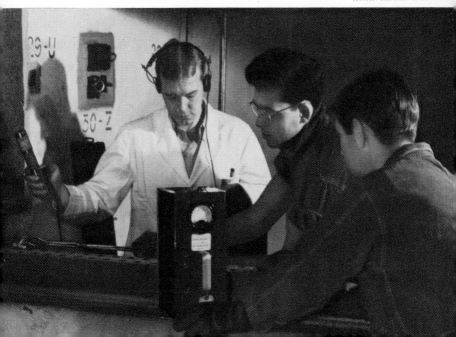

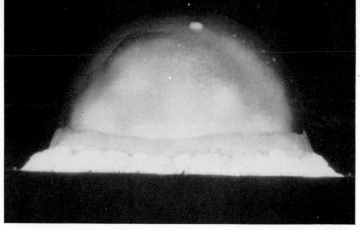

*"Bubble, bubble, toil and trouble." The seething blister of
the trial atomic bomb, Alamogordo, N. M., July 16, 1945.*

larger speck. These were enough to prove the Bohr-
Wheeler theory.

It was the less than 1% of U-235 in uranium which
was the stuff out of which an atomic bomb might be
made. The thing now was possible, yet only remotely
possible, for it would take twelve million years by
these methods to produce one pound of U-235. Much
more than a pound would be needed for one bomb.

Hitler was about to invade Poland. World War II
would bring on a silent, deadly contest to find a
means of making U-235 in quantities. The winner
would win the war almost surely, for there could be
no doubt about the paralyzing effect, physically and
morally, of even one bomb. That this was true, however, was known in the United States only to a number of scientists.

In the terms of a detective story, the murderer now
was identified and the case against him completed by
the police. But the facts and the alleged motive were

fantastic, beyond the experience of normal people, and a jury remained to be convinced.

Before the war began, Dr. Pegram sent Dr. Fermi to Washington to warn our Government of the military possibilities of the discovery. Everyone with whom he talked was interested, the Navy especially so. No one scoffed at his warning, yet nothing tangible came of his visit and so in August, 1939, Dr. Einstein wrote a letter to the President.

"In the course of the past four months," he wrote, "it has been made probable that a nuclear chain reaction can be set up in a large mass of uranium, by which vast amounts of power and large quantities of new radium-like elements would be generated. Now it appears almost certain that this could be achieved in the immediate future. This new phenomenon also would lead to the construction of bombs, and it is conceivable—though much less certain—that extremely powerful bombs of a new type, carried by boat or exploded in a port, might well destroy the whole port together with some of the surrounding territory. However, such bombs might very well prove to be too heavy for transport by air."

Note Dr. Einstein's doubt in 1939 that any airplane could carry an atomic bomb. How large were the atomic bombs dropped on Japan still is a secret, but London newspapers have said, whether true or not, that they weighed four tons each and were so long that only a B-29 Superfortress, not yet in existence in 1939, could carry one.

The President called in one of his aides, naming him as liaison officer for the White House and appointed a committee which soon met. Dissatisfied with the results, Dr. Einstein wrote the President a second letter in the spring of 1940. When France fell that May, President Roosevelt created the Office of Scientific Research and Development under Dr. Vannevar Bush, which took over the atomic project.

By that summer Germany commonly was supposed to be as much as a year ahead of the British and us in this pursuit, and the British spent many lives in two Commando raids in Norway with the single purpose of destroying a "heavy water" plant being operated there by the Nazis, and discovering the results. To scientists, "heavy water" spelled atomic bomb; it is a compound of hydrogen, the moderator used by Fermi to slow his neutrons.

In this country a voluntary censorship was imposed almost a year before Pearl Harbor, and atomic fission was never spoken of publicly. But laboratory research had gone so far by June of 1942, when an atomic bomb still was a comic strip phantasy to most of us, that Dr. Bush was able to report to the White House that an explosion equal to "many thousand tons of TNT" could be "caused at a desired moment by the fission or explosion of U-235," and that enough U-235 for a bomb could be made by any one of four different methods.

It could be done by turning uranium into a gas and filtering the lighter U-235 isotope away from the

The trial New Mexican bomb photographed from ten miles away. The photographer wore arc-welder's glasses to shield his eyes from the searing light.

heavier U-238. Or the separation could be done electromagnetically or by heat or with centrifuges. (The dairyman's cream separator is a form of centrifuge).

The Hiroshima bomb first became a definite possibility on December 6, 1942, nearly a year after Pearl Harbor, when the first chain reaction in history was set off under controlled conditions in a "pile" built on a squash court beneath the stands of Stagg Field, University of Chicago's stadium. That is to say that more neutrons were released than were used up in starting the explosion, and the process perpetuated itself.

The government at once ordered plants built for all four processes on the great scale necessary to collect enough U-235 for a bomb, and had spent more than a billion and a half dollars on this top war secret before Hiroshima was blasted as if hit by a comet.

There were no provisions for cooling in the Chicago pile and so it was operated at low energy, but it provided the technical information needed to set up a larger U-235 pile at Oak Ridge, Tennessee, and the far greater ones at Hanford, Washington, which made the plutonium which went into one or more bombs.

Plutonium? What is that? Even before December, 1942, it had been discovered at the University of California that uranium when bombarded with slow neutrons was transmuted in part into a new man-made element, christened plutonium, with similar properties to U-235. But all the plutonium the Berkeley cyclotron could produce in the year 1942 was 500 micrograms, equal in size to the head of a pin. Plutonium may exist in other worlds, but it never had been found in ours.

It isn't that plutonium or U-235 are the only fissionable elements. The nucleus of the atom of any element heavier than silver can be broken down, re-

"Few can ever know how frightening was the responsibility of Maj. Gen. Leslie R. Groves," who commanded the Manhattan Project.

leasing not much less hidden energy than does uranium. The special quality of 235 and plutonium is a hair trigger. It would be so difficult to burst the atom of any element but uranium, thorium, plutonium and protoactinium that scientists can not yet foresee a time when an atomic bomb may be made from other elements.

What is called a "pile" for lack of a better word is a mass of graphite. Graphite is one of several possible moderators, and a moderator is, of course, something that will slow a neutron down, a brake, increasing its probability of hitting a nucleus squarely on the button. Oddly, while the Germans used an American discovery, heavy water, we chose pure carbon, which is graphite.

Just the getting of enough pure carbon and uranium for a small pile was a critical problem in 1941, one on which the American chemical industry concentrated. A cube pile of uranium oxide and graphite completed at Columbia University in July, 1941, failed to work. There were enough impurities in the uranium oxide to block the reaction. There were only a few grams of pure uranium metal in all the world then, yet by 1942 we had produced the several tons which went into the successful University of Chicago pile.

The Eldorado pitchblende mines north of the Arctic Circle in the Canadian wilds are the principal American source of uranium, and they are frozen in except for a few weeks of midsummer. In the nick of time, the Manhattan District by telephone contracted for the mines' entire output for a year. The last boat was about to steam up the Mackenzie river before it closed for navigation, and the Eldorado Company barely had time to recruit a force of miners and load a winter's stores of food aboard the river steamer.

A little later the Manhattan District learned of a large stock of uranium ore already mined and stored above ground, deep in the interior of the Belgian Congo. The Nazis were in North Africa and feinting toward Dakar, making the west coast unsafe. The uranium ore stockpile was bought by radio, shipped by rail to Africa's east coast and thence by steamer around the southern tips of Africa and South America and to San Francisco.

In the University of Chicago pile the few tons of uranium metal then to be had was mixed with uranium oxide and scattered at carefully calculated distances throughout the graphite matrix. What happened then? Given an outside trigger source, supplied by a trifle of pure U-235, some of the 235 nuclei in the uranium in the pile were split in the next fraction of a second. One million split 235 nuclei would re-

"The beginning or the end—." *The Hiroshima bomb burst photographed from the B-29 Enola Gay, which dropped the bomb.*

Hiroshima—Before

lease between one and three million more neutron bullets. Some of these escaped from the pile and were lost, more were captured and disarmed by the many 238 nuclei, others by impurities. But on the average, a million of these new neutrons smashed another million 235 nuclei in the next fraction of a second to maintain the production rate.

These explosions were throttled down with bars of

—*After*

cadmium or of boron steel passed completely through the pile in slots, these neutron-resistant metals holding the produced energy down to a weak one half of one watt. The energy appeared first in the 6,000-miles-a-second speed of the neutrons thrown off, then was converted into sensible heat as collisions slowed down these projectiles to the pace of a strolling man.

As soon as more graphite and uranium metal were

to be had, the duPont company built for the Government at Oak Ridge an air-cooled 1,000-kilowatt chain-reaction pile operated by University of Chicago physicists. Instead of spotting the uranium in the graphite like raisins in a cookie, here for the first time uranium rods were sealed in aluminum cylinders and inserted in channels in the graphite. Removal of some of the rods slowed down the process, the adding of rods speeded it up. Both the size of the rods and their spacing were delicate problems in mathematical physics. An error either would defeat the process or cause an uncontrolled explosion.

Though this was a sizeable plant, it would, operating continuously for one year, split only a few pounds of 235 and only about one thousandth of the mass of

"One of our cities is missing." Of Hiroshima's 90,000 buildings, 62,000 were destroyed and 6,000 more damaged beyond repair.

uranium nuclei would be converted into energy. It and a plutonium plant built a few miles west of Chicago in Argonne Forest served as pilots for the Hanford works.

The huge Hanford plant, producing only plutonium, was begun early in 1943 on some 1,000 miles of sage brush and sand in Eastern Washington taken over by the Government. Hanford, a village of 436, ballooned to a population of 51,000 and now is entirely deserted. Richland, even smaller in 1941 than Hanford, now is a town of 15,000 and the permanent headquarters of the plutonium works.

The plutonium plant was to have been built at Oak Ridge like the others, but its dangers seemed so great that a more isolated spot was sought. Too, the process needed the abundant supply of cold water for cooling to be had from the Columbia river. By the time the three piles were running there in the spring of 1945, the atomic heat generated had raised the temperature of the river fractionally, although the cooling water undergoes a long period of decontamination before being turned back into the Columbia.

The U-235 was supplied by the gaseous diffusion, electromagnetic and thermal diffusion plants in Tennessee. Though they were put in the Clinch river valley primarily in order to tap the nearby TVA power, one of the world's greatest steam power plants also was erected alongside the gaseous diffusion works. The thermal diffusion plant was closed down after the war, the centrifuge works dropped early; the

Steel-concrete buildings were crushed at a distance from the Hiroshima blast center where the bomb's force was estimated at 8 tons per square yard.

other two continue to operate twenty-four hours a day.

Chrysler Corporation built the diffusers for the gas plant. It consists of 63 buildings at Oak Ridge costing half a billion dollars, the principal one a strange 4-story, windowless U-shaped structure, 2,500 feet long and 400 feet wide. It is the world's greatest continuous chemcophysical process factory. The process was developed at Columbia University, the plant designed and built by the Kellex Corporation and operated by Union Carbide & Carbon.

A trailer moved onto the Oak Ridge site July 3, 1943, housing the original settlers of what in another year had become Tennessee's fifth city. Ground was broken for the first process buildings of the gas plant in September, and though producing 235 atoms well before, the entire plant had not been finished at the war's end. It is an agonizingly slow process and there was a long, long search by a large and able group of experts for a feasible way of mass-producing the "barrier" material.

This was one of many instances in which General Groves gambled courageously on ultimate success. The Manhattan Project had spent a quarter of a billion dollars on the gas plant before the barrier production problem was whipped. Without the barrier stuff, the plant would have been useless, yet had Manhattan held back until this problem was solved, Oak Ridge would have produced no 235 before 1946. As it was, the plant was waiting for the diffuser equipment as it began to arrive in quantities.

In this process, uranium is converted into a gas, the fiercely corrosive uranium hexafluoride. The plant is operated under an extremely tight vacuum, the gas pumped through the filters or barrier material. The molecules of the U-235 isotope being lighter than those of 238, travel faster and penetrate the faintly porous barrier more often. So for a while the gas on the far side of the barrier will be richer in 235. This is drawn off and recycled. After thousands of repetitions taking many days you get a rich concentration of U-235.

It is necessary to start tens of thousands times the

quantity of gas finally delivered as the enriched product. Enormous quantities of the microscopically porous barrier stuff were needed. As finally worked out, this material resisted the devouring hexafluoride better than stainless steel resists ordinary air.

As any leak would halt the process, the plant was built to incredible tightness. In power-plant practice, a vacuum of 1-inch of mercury is very good. Here was a vacuum *twenty-five million* times greater. If the plant were to be shut down today, be sealed and allowed to stand in a non-corrosive atmosphere, few who are reading this would live to see the vacuum completely broken down.

To create such a void of air, unheard of quantities of pumps were needed. Pumps were operated here for the first time at a speed beyond that of sound. More than 25,000 man-hours of research went into the pump problem alone, revolutionizing pump technology.

An entirely new technique of cutting and welding glass pipe was developed, making it possible to duplicate in glass anything an expert pipefitter can do with steel, and even to add a trick impossible in metal.

In the nearby electromagnetic plant a uranium gas is electrified by passing it through an electric arc. These ionized uranium atoms then are passed through an electric field which accelerates them to a speed of many thousand miles a second. At this tremendous speed the mixed 238 and 235 atoms enter an intensely strong magnetic field which curves them into circular

The first plutonium bomb; the Nagasaki burst mushrooming into the stratosphere. A wing of the photograph ship shows at lower right.

COLORED U. S. A. A. F. PHOTO

33

paths. The lighter 235 atoms are deflected more than the 238 and half-way around their race track a splitter divides the two streams. Again, many, many repetitions are necessary before a nearly pure U-235 metal results.

The success of the separation depends upon the acute sharpness of the focus of the two magnetic beams and this hinges in turn upon the precision of the magnetic field. The specification limited the variation in the field to 1 part in 5,000, a uniformity believed impossible by many.

The electro-magnets are 250 feet long, containing thousands of tons of special steel; a hundred times bigger than that in the 184-inch cyclotron at the University of California, until then the world's greatest. Their pull on the nails in the shoes of the workers made walking difficult. A carpenter had to clutch a nail tightly to keep it from twisting out of his fingers. An ordinary wrench either would be wrested from a man's hand, or, if he clung to it, he would be banged against the magnetic face. This was avoided by the use of non-magnetic steels in tools and nearby equipment.

At the Hanford works where the plutonium is recovered chemically from thirty or so radioactive by-products, all very dangerous, this is done by complex, remotely-controlled and nearly automatic machinery, much of it installed underground. The radioactivity of any one of Hanford's three piles is equal roughly to that given off by a million pounds of radium—and all

*Wreckage of the Mitsubishi steel plant at
Nagasaki on the outer fringes of the bomb's fury.*

the radium man has isolated so far amounts to about
two pounds.

The plutonium process was developed and the
Hanford works designed on the results of experiments
using only one millionth of a gram of plutonium. One
thousandth of a gram is invisible to the eye; a millionth of a gram weighs less than a baby's breath.
There chemical engineers had to deal with a brand
new element, its chemistry, physical properties and
constants all unknown.

Each of the Hanford piles contains many thousand
blocks of graphite machined to such precision that
the over-all structures are accurate to machine shop

35

standards. The holes in the graphite holding the uranium slugs have the accuracy of rifle barrels. The amount of plutonium recovered in the chemical separation is little more than the percentage of natural lime in the river water used to make the solution. These mountains produce molehills, hence their huge size.

Oak Ridge is served by spurs of the Southern and the Louisville & Nashville railroads. When the two roads had moved in some 50,000 car lots of materials and gotten back only empty cars, it is said that a freight agent for one road called at the headquarters building.

"One of these days you will be moving out a lot of tonnage and we hope we are going to get our share of this traffic," he said.

He was told to be patient. When 100,000 cars had been shunted in and 100,000 empties hauled away, the freight agent paid a second call. Again he was told to be patient. By the time the railroads had delivered 150,000 car loads and had gotten back nothing but rolling stock, the general freight agent is supposed to have investigated.

"You are getting the business whether you can see it or not," they told him.

And so they were. The product of more than a billion dollars spent at Oak Ridge alone was leaving there in nothing bigger than a brief case, each carried by a messenger. The messengers had no idea what they were transporting. Each was sent by a new route

Fused glass in ruins of a Nagasaki medical school, half a mile from the blast center. The bomb's heat was estimated at 6,000 degrees.

to a new destination, though the powder was destined always either for the Hanford works or for Los Alamos, New Mexico.

You have heard less about Los Alamos, a New Mexican mesa some 30 miles from Santa Fe, that was a boys' ranch school until 1942, than of Oak Ridge and of Hanford because it is there that Dr. J. Robert Oppenheimer and a large staff of scientists worked out the technique of forming and exploding the bombs. This continues to be the top secret.

Any other explosive can be tested safely in small amounts, but a small-scale atomic bomb would be no bomb at all. U-235 or plutonium are no more automatically explosive than so much sand until the quantity reaches a certain size and shape. Hence the bombs had to be the product of pure calculation on the part of the theoretical physics division at Los Alamos.

If, for a given shape there is a critical weight and the stuff explodes instantly when this weight is reached, how could man postpone the explosion until a desired moment? The obvious way would be to divide the bomb into two or more well-separated parts, bringing them together at the chosen moment with gunpowder or some other convenient force. The

Nagasaki steel work half a mile from the blast center was smashed in as if by a giant's sledge-hammer.

famous Smyth report published a few days after Hiroshima indicates that some sort of gun barrel shot one section of the mass at the other, the gun being fired by a time fuse which went into action when the bomb was dropped from the plane.

The true secret of the atomic bomb, however, was exposed in the next few moments after the Superfortress "Enola Gay" opened its bomb bay doors over Hiroshima. For the greatest secret of all was to keep all knowledge of the bomb's imminence from the enemy. A first necessity of this was to limit all knowledge of Oak Ridge, Hanford and Los Alamos to as few as possible.

Billion dollar plants employing tens of thousands of workers are hard to hide, but "cat fur to make kitten britches" can be a better defense against curiosity than hard looks or threats. "Blackout paint for lightning bugs" was a favorite jest at Oak Ridge, and some anonymous local humorist wrote a burlesque secret document which was circulated in the thousands of copies. It read:

"PROCESS

"They are taking plumscrate, raw plumscrate mind you, and putting it into ballisportle tanks. These are called ballisportle tanks because the inside is coated with quadrelstitle and this preserves the full strength of the plumscrate. Next, this is taken to the sarraputing room where only expert sarraputers are employed. At this point of course is when they add thungborium, the ingredient which causes the entire masterfuge to Knoxify and then after spurndazzle is applied the entire product disappears. This invisible compound is later transferred to the abblesnurting building where glass snagglehooks are applied for carrying. This completes the manufacturing operation and delivery is the next problem.

"At 12:20 on the third Tuesday night of each month, 800 men known as shizzlefrinks because their brains have been siphoned from their heads, are lined up in single file, each given two ingots of oustenstufftingle (name of the finished product) and away they march over the hills to Fakima where they trade the finished product for enough raw material to make another batch of oustenstufftingle.

SECRET"

Several hundred thousand men and women in America had a part in the bomb, but the project was so compartmentalized, both in the plants and research laboratories, that few learned more than was essential to his own task. It was a rare American who had any faint inkling of what was coming even after the trial bomb had been proven in the dawn of July 16, 1945, in New Mexico, or understood what the President of the United States and the Premier of Great Britain were saying ten days later when, at Potsdam, they issued a surrender ultimatum to Japan.

How well the secret was kept even from some professionals is indicated by a prediction made by Dr.

Bikini's chief and his queen; they and their people were removed to another Pacific atoll before Operations Crossroads.

Kai Seigbahn, Swedish physicist of world repute. The Berlin radio had quoted the High Command as threatening, in retaliation for the mass bombing of German cities, "by one fell, drastic stroke to end this unbridled mass murder," adding that "mankind is not far from the point where it can at will blow up half the globe."

To any physicist this meant the atomic bomb, but Dr. Siegbahn commented: "Despite all the secretiveness about research into the uranium problem, I venture to say that the uranium bomb still is nonexistent except as a research objective."

41

The Japanese premier was another skeptic. He contemptuously dismissed the Truman-Bevin ultimatum on July 29th. Eight days later Hiroshima was annihilated and in another three days a second bomb fell on Nagasaki.

The following day the Swiss Charge d'Affaires at Washington, acting for Tokyo, notified our State Department of Japan's acceptance of the Potsdam terms. Formal surrender followed in three days more.

This was two and a half months prior to the date fixed for our invasion of the Japanese mainland in force.

By the estimates of the Army and Navy we were saved as many as one million casualties.

At her surrender, Japan had more than 9,000 planes in the home islands available for Kamikaze attack, of which more than 5,000 already had been specially fitted for these suicide tactics against our expected invasion. This was no idle threat. At Okinawa nearly 20% of all Kamikaze missions had been effective. Though no ship of ours larger than an escort carrier ever was sunk by the Kamikazes, fifteen battleships, twelve carriers and sixteen escort carriers were damaged. Misled by their own exaggerated claims of heavy ships sunk, the Japs fortunately had ignored the advice of their technicians that a heavier explosive head was needed to sink capital ships, or our losses would have been severe indeed.

Think of the appalling ease with which two cities were destroyed and a war decided. To drop 2,000 tons of ordinary high explosives or incendiaries on a

Blasting coral ledges out of Bikini lagoon before Operations Cross-roads. Contrast the feeble power of explosives with atomic fission.

Japanese target, with greatly less destruction, had taken sorties of 300 or more B-29 Superfortresses.

One group, the 509th, dropped both bombs on Japan. There are only thirty planes in a group and only two of the thirty were used.

The 509th had been the 393rd Bombardment Squadron, had completed two-thirds of its training

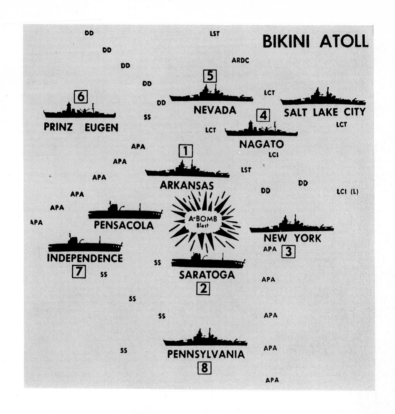

at a Nebraska field and was preparing to be sent overseas for straight bombardment work when it was detached in October, 1944, and sent to Wendover Field, on the salt flats at the Utah-Nevada line to train for a "highly secret job," described only as one which, if successful, might shorten the war by a year or more.

As they were equipped with Superforts from the Martin-Nebraska assembly plant at Omaha, it may be inferred that they had Dodge-Chicago built engines and Chrysler-made nose sections. It is known

44

definitely that "The Great Artiste", which dropped the plutonium bomb on Nagasaki, was B-29 No. 42-7353, assembled at Omaha. In January, 1945, the first ten planes were dispatched to Batista Field, Cuba, for long, simulated combat missions against Borinquen Field, Puerto Rico; the Virgin Isles, Bermuda and Norfolk.

All but the crews left San Francisco on the transport, Cape Victory, May 6th, joining a convoy at Honolulu, putting in at Eniwetok nine days later and landing on Tinian Memorial Day morning. The

The first flash of the Test Able plutonium bomb as photographed from a robot "drone" plane, crusing over the lagoon, June 30, 1946.

Bomb No. 4 explodes over the guinea-pig fleet of 73 warships anchored in Bikini lagoon, June 30, 1946.

COLORED U. S. A. A. F. PHOTO

planes followed in June and early July, bringing the group to 1,500 men and 200 officers.

Orders for a strike against the Jap homeland were issued July 19th. "This is it," the word ran through Tinian, but it and three more missions carried out by flights of eight to eleven B-29's were ordinary bombing runs to familiarize the crews with their coming task.

Three planes, the Enola Gay and a photographic and an instrument ship, took off under flood lights from Tinian at half past two of an August Sunday morning, dropping the Hiroshima bomb at 8:15 Japanese time of that sunny morning.

"One of our cities is missing" gasped a gunner. The awesome result was reported to Tinian by coded radio and when the Enola Gay put down at 3 P.M., a loud speaker commanded "Attention to orders!" General Carl A. (Tooey) Spaatz stepped forward and pinned the Distinguished Service Cross on Colonel Tibbett's chest.

Three days later the B-29 Great Artiste, which had flown right wing as instrument ship to the Enola Gay on the Hiroshima mission, took off for Kokura— which never has been publicly identified by the Government. This time the weather was bad and the primary target "socked in". The anti-aircraft fire also was severe. After losing an hour seeking a break in the clouds, the Great Artiste, low on gas, turned to unlucky Nagasaki, its secondary target, finding it by radar. The clouds here parted at the last

*The light carrier Independence still smould-
ering after the first Bikini air-burst bomb.*

moment and Captain Kermit K. Behan dropped the
bomb visually. This was the first plutonium bomb
and the shock felt by the Great Artiste was much
greater. Refueling at Okinawa, the crew were home
well in time to attend a dance for three hundred
Army nurses just landed on Tinian.

There was no anti-aircraft fire and no interceptor
attack either at Hiroshima or Nagasaki. Our B-29's
long had been using Lake Biwa, northeast of Hiroshima, as a rendezvous point in their massed attacks
on Jap cities so alarms had been constant in Hiroshima. But no bomb ever had been dropped there
and an American weather plane came over every
morning at about this hour.

49

Seeing only one B-san or Mister B, as the Japs had come to call the Superfort, at a high altitude that morning, the air wardens had sounded the usual alert —heeded by relatively few—and then, satisfied that it was the morning weather plane as usual, blown the All Clear a minute or two before the atomic bomb burst, killing many as they emerged from shelters.

Mica, the melting point of which is 900 degrees, was found fused on gravestones a thousand feet from the center of the blast. The bomb's heat on the ground at its center was estimated by the Japanese at 6,000 degrees, its force at 5.3 to 8 tons per square yard.

In November the Japs reported the Hiroshima casualties as 78,150 killed, 13,983 missing and 37,425 injured, but these figures went on growing. Of 90,000 buildings in a city that had been chosen as Imperial headquarters in the event we should invade Japan and capture Tokyo, 62,000 were destroyed and 6,000 more damaged beyond repair. Only five modern buildings in the city's heart survived in a condition that allowed their use without major reconstruction.

The mangled stern of the Independence.

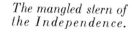

Two dozen men who suffered no scratch had killed or injured some 300,000 Japanese. In the whole war our dead and missing, exclusive of disease and rear area accidents, was only 225,000. In the two and a half months we were driving the Germans from the Normandy beaches to their own frontier, Hitler's forces lost only 200,000 in dead and wounded. Battles as deadly as the Somme or Ypres of World War I, both drawn out for months, were won in seconds with the tripping of a lever. Our world could never be the same again.

* * * * *

Colonel Ed. Garbisch of the Corps of Engineers, one-time West Point football star and a son-in-law of the late Walter Chrysler, phoned Mr. Keller on March 20, 1943, on behalf of Colonel J. C. Marshall of the Manhattan District, who wished to see Chrysler's president. The latter never had heard of the Manhattan District or of Colonel Marshall, but Colonel Garbisch said that it was important. Colonel Marshall's errand was not disclosed.

An appointment was made for April 2nd in Detroit. The visitors, led by Maj. Gen. L. R. Groves, head of the Manhattan District, withheld nothing from the Chrysler group composed of B. E. Hutchinson, H. L. Weckler, Fred L. Zeder, Nicholas Kelley and Mr. Keller, none of whom had heard until then of atomic fission other than as a scientific dream. To laymen, the thing sounded almost incredibly fantastic, but if the United States Government thought it practicable, this, Mr. Keller said, was all that the Corporation needed to know.

In any case, Chrysler's job would have nothing to do with nuclear physics. The gaseous diffusion method of separating U-235 from uranium was described and Chrysler asked to undertake the design and manufacture of the large metal diffusers, a problem which the Government felt needed the research and manufacturing resources of the Corporation. It would be a $75,000,000 contract.

The gas was so corrosive, it was explained, that only one group of metals would resist it, and only one of this group, nickel, is reasonably commercial in price and supply. The Government specified that the diffusers should be made of solid nickel.

The containers necessarily would be big and many thousands of them would be wanted. (As designed by Chrysler, they looked something like an anchor buoy, or an oversized depth bomb, or a poison gas drum.) A quick calculation indicated that the first order would eat up all the nickel mined in America for two years—though nickel is not a scarce metal.

As no such supply was to be had, Mr. Keller suggested electroplating nickel on steel, using no more than a thousandth as much nickel. But no plating would resist the hexafluoride gas, according to expert testimony; any plating would peel off and the gas then would devour the steel.

To Chrysler, which knew nothing about uranium hexafluoride but a great deal about nickel plating,

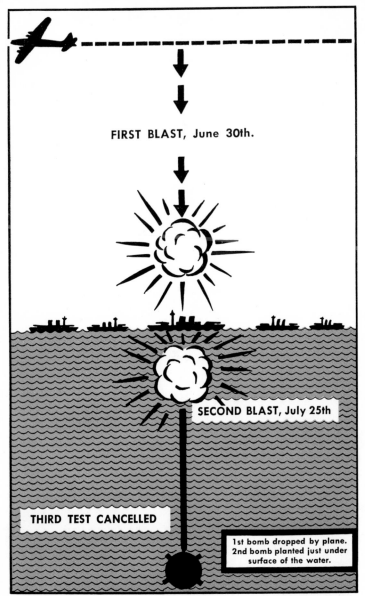

FIRST BLAST, June 30th.

SECOND BLAST, July 25th

THIRD TEST CANCELLED

1st bomb dropped by plane.
2nd bomb planted just under
surface of the water.

this seemed improbable. A plating should resist anything which solid nickel resists if the plating was pure and the bond a good one, because the metal's resistance has nothing to do with its depth. Mr. Keller had great confidence in the Chrysler Engineering plating laboratory and its director, Carl E. Heussner, which never had failed the Corporation and which had been working as the war began on a new plating process of promise.

So when the Corporation put J. M. Hartgering in charge of this new war job and sent him to New York to study the gaseous diffusion pilot plant at Columbia University, it sent Heussner with him. They found New York unconcerned about the staggering quantities of nickel needed, taking it for granted that the project's exalted directive would provide anything it asked. As for plating, no plating could be held under

What the air-burst Bikini bomb did COLORED ASSOCIATED PRESS
to the surfaced submarine "Skate".

The old battleship Nevada in place at Bikini for the Test Able and Test Baker bombs.

these conditions, the laboratory men repeated. Not until the second day would they agree to humor Heussner to the extent of promising to test his plating samples in the gas chamber.

He hurried back to Detroit to prepare his samples and to get control samples of pure nickel from the International Nickel Co., and was ready within a week. When his plating was exposed to uranium hexafluoride it withstood the gas even better than the pure control samples, as Heussner had been confident it would. The so-called pure nickel of commerce contains about 1% of impurities; in the electro-plating process very little of this 1% of foreign matter is transferred to the plate, and so the latter is a little the purer of the two.

Without waiting for the Columbia laboratory report, Mr. Keller told Heussner to run a full-scale test, plating a large shell with enough of a set-up to be sure

This photograph was made from a drone flying directly over Test Baker.

of a first-rate job. Heussner was lent some space in the Highland Park plant where a pit was dug for a plating bath. He chose for the test as unpromising a piece of material as lay at hand, a sheet of old boiler plate. Cleaning and welding it into a cylinder, he covered it with a thin coating of nickel with the same success he had had with his samples. All that was needed was a good mechanical bond and all that is required for such a bond is a good, clean, active surface.

No hexafluoride gas was available in Detroit for a test, but he was in doubt only about the porosity of the plating and this he checked by immersing it in hot water mixed with carbon dioxide. This same hot water-carbon dioxide bath was used as a control test in the early months of manufacture, but the plating was so successful from the first that the Government shortly ordered this test discontinued.

This great saving of nickel was the Corporation's most notable contribution to the atomic bomb. But for Chrysler's demonstration that the diffusers could be made with a thin plating, it is unlikely that an atomic bomb could have been dropped on Japan as early as August of 1945, for sheer lack of nickel.

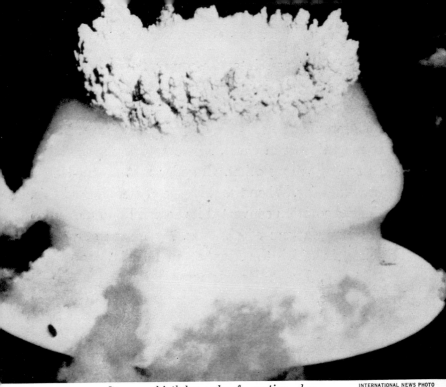

Strange birthday-cake formation during early stages of Baker explosion.

The F.B.I. and Army Intelligence moved in with a security patrol, but keeping such a secret within a large corporation called for unusual precautions on the Corporation's part. Driving down Woodward Avenue, Mr. Keller noticed the vacant department store building at 1525 in Detroit's downtown, the first floor of which temporarily was housing the current bond drive headquarters. Vacant space in Detroit during the war was precious, and Keller's first act on returning to his office was to order the place rented. The bond drive continued to use the ground floor, conveniently masking Chrysler's secret. All Chrysler personnel assigned to X-100 moved into the upper floors, which the Corporation continued to occupy for nearly two years.

More than half a million feet of manufacturing space would be needed and the building must be unusually tight and clean. Manufacturing space being as scarce as any other, Chrysler first planned on a new building. When the shortage of steel balked this, the Corporation converted its Lynch Road factory to the manufacture of diffusers. By means of various shifts, in which the Manhattan District cooperated helpfully, Lynch Road's normal jobs were moved elsewhere. Its truck operations were transferred to a new, though much smaller building, authorized as an addition to the Dodge Truck plant. The elimination of all organic matter—which is one way of saying "absolute cleanliness"—being a necessity to the defeat of hexafluoride, the entire assembly section in the remodeled Lynch Road factory was air-conditioned. Chrysler had been required to make a quick estimate of the cost of converting the plant, a figure the Corporation later reduced voluntarily by nearly $400,000 as a result of economies found possible.

Welding nickel plate is a cranky job and a vast amount of welding went into the fabricated assembly. Among many details, Lynch Road had to drill 50 million holes held to very close limits and very accurately placed in relation one to another. In order to get an absolutely even nickel coating throughout, it was necessary to radius burr each of these millions of holes at both ends. New kinds of machinery had

*Unbelievable—a column of water a half
a mile wide and thousands of feet high.*

to be designed. In all, Lynch Road shipped more
than a thousand carloads of finished apparatus
to Oak Ridge, plated a surface equal to many acres.

When Mr. Keller walked into the plant the morning of August 7, 1945, to deliver the congratulations
of General Groves, a couple of smiling foremen
greeted him knowingly with "We dood it." Many
wore a knowing look as if the bomb had been no
secret to them. The fact was, however, that except
for Mr. Hartgering; his chief engineer, Alan Loof-

burrow; his assistant works manager, Ralph Jones; his designing engineer, David Tooth; the superintendent of final testing, John Hutchinson; and Charles Heinan and Charles Morris of the engineering staff, most of whom had visited Oak Ridge, probably no one had a remote idea of the purpose of the job until he read the morning papers of August 7th, and many had failed then to realize that this was the fruit of their work. For that matter, many high officials of the Corporation knew no more about X-100 than that it was a dangerous secret.

In giving the job a code name, Chrysler had followed Manhattan District practice. In the entire Manhattan project the word uranium never was used; its code designation was *tubealloy*. The numbers 235 and 238 were taboo, always represented by the letters X and Y. No parts of the critical apparatus, nor any plant or building or responsible officer ever was referred to in writing or by telephone except by code.

Every employee of Lynch Road and of 1525 Woodward, not excepting janitors and office girls or Mr. Keller and Mr. Zeder, was methodically investigated by Army Intelligence or the F.B.I., and signed a security agreement not to talk. While this precaution was wise, what any of them could have disclosed usually would have been more misleading than useful to an enemy agent. Human curiosity being what it is, their minds naturally speculated about the secret and as naturally reached the common conclusion that the plant was making materials for rocket bombs

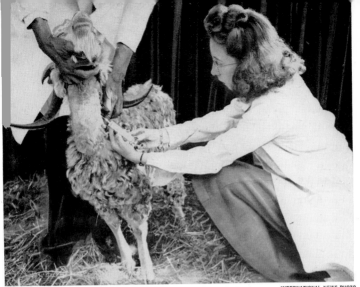

Goat survivor of two Bikini bombs, returned to America, submits to blood sampling for radiation effects at University of Chicago.

similar to the German V-1 and V-2, these secret weapons being the sensation of the moment. The better informed risked being misled by their own technical knowledge. For example, chemists on the laboratory staff, knowing that they were dealing with fluorine, assumed that the project was making poison gas, all the fluorine gases being deadly.

Mr. Keller had with him that morning, too, a telegram from Robert F. Patterson, then Under Secretary of War, which read: "Today the whole world knows the secret you have helped us to keep for many months. I am pleased to be able to add that the war lords of Japan now know its effect even better than we ourselves. The atomic bomb you have helped to develop with high devotion to patriotic duty is the most devastating military weapon that any country

Beyond Imagination. The under-water burst at Bikini photographed from the beach by automatic cameras that were undamaged.

COLORED INTERNATIONAL NEWS PHOTO

J. M. Hartgering, Works Manager of the Chrysler X-100 Plant.

ever has been able to turn against an enemy. No one of you has worked on the entire project or has known the whole story. Each of you has done his own job and kept his own secret and so today I speak for a grateful nation when I say we are proud of every one of you."

Chrysler's role was described in detail at the atomic bomb award dinner given by the Chemical and Metallurgical Engineering Society February 26, 1946, by P. C. Keith, who had been technical director of the Kellex Company, which built the gaseous diffusion works.

"The manufacture of the diffusers was hardly attractive business for the overworked industrialist," Mr. Keith told the audience. "Nevertheless, the Chrysler Corporation agreed to undertake it. While patiently awaiting the solution of the barrier material problem, they tooled up an efficient assembly line and manufactured some of the parts. They also studied the mechanical properties of available specimens of barrier, devised methods of fabricating the barrier into a gas-tight sub-assembly, and carried on extensive research and development along related lines. As a result, when the barrier finally was available, they were able to turn out diffusers in record time. It may now be revealed to their credit, and to the credit of the engineers at Oak Ridge, that all but two of the thousands of units manufactured for installation at Oak Ridge were actually set up and operated."

The research mentioned by Mr. Keith was carried out by a force of 170 technicians assigned to Lynch Road from the Chrysler Engineering Division.

A letter which went into the Keller scrap book was written by General Groves at Christmas of 1945. "No one outside the K-25 portion of the project," wrote the project's director, "can ever know how much we depended upon you and how well you performed. Those of us who do know will never forget how im-

A part of the diffuser plating line in the remodelled Chrysler Lynch Road plant.

portant your work was and how well you did it."

Few can ever know, either, how frightening was the responsibility of General Groves and how well he performed. There had been a time when Under Secretary Patterson, growing uneasy about an expense that had passed the billion dollar mark, sent out a confidential emissary to look over Oak Ridge, Los Alamos and Hanford.

When the emissary returned to Washington, the Under Secretary, expecting a lengthy report, sent word that he could not see him that day, but would set aside the next afternoon to hear the report. The confidential investigator sent back word that he could speak his piece in one minute flat, and so he was ushered in at once.

"If it works," he told Secretary Patterson, "no one will ever investigate its cost; if it doesn't work, they'll investigate nothing else."

Co-hero of the bomb with General Groves was Dr. Vannevar Bush, director of the Office of Scientific Research and Development, under which name the scientific brains of America were mobilized for war. The atomic bomb was one detail of its vast labors, the record of which fills 2,500,000 volumes, or almost enough to stock the New York public library.

As for Lynch Road, reconverted to peace, it now is making axles for Chrysler Corporation cars and trucks.

The gallant carrier Saratoga, survivor of the air-burst Bikini bomb, slowly settles to the bottom after the under-water burst.

67